ONE MORE TIME 2
POPS FOR PARTIES

CONTENTS

First Published 1986

© International Music Publications Limited
  Southend Road, Woodford Green
  Essex IG8 8HN, England

215-2-349

Medley 1

AGADOO

Words and Music by M. SYMILE
M. DELANCERY and J. PERAM

A - ga -

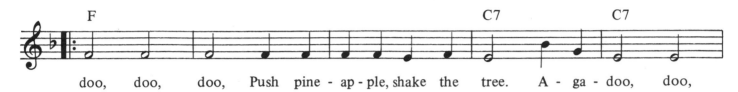

doo, doo, doo, Push pine - ap - ple, shake the tree. A - ga-doo, doo,

doo, Push pine - ap - ple, grind cof - fee. To the left, to the right, Jump up and

down and to the knees.. Come and dance ev - 'ry night. Sing with a Hu - la mel - o -

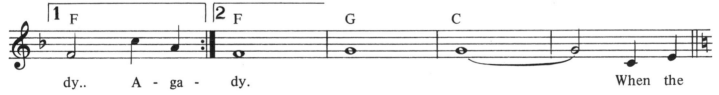

dy.. A - ga - dy.

LA PALOMA BLANCA

Words and Music by
J. BOUWENS

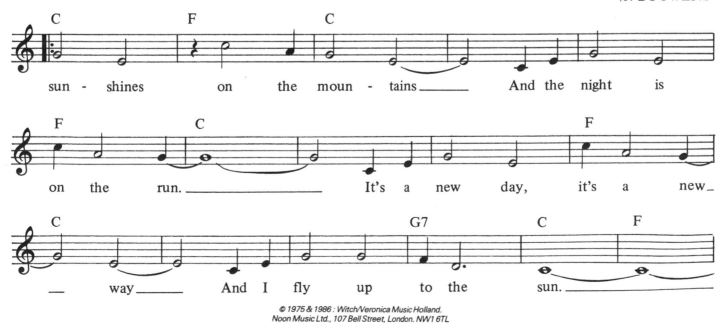

sun - shines on the moun - tains ___ And the night is

on the run. ___ It's a new day, it's a new ___

___ way ___ And I fly up to the sun. ___

COPACABANA (AT THE COPA)

Words by BRUCE SUSSMAN and JACK FELDMAN
Music by BARRY MANILOW

Medley 2

SONG SUNG BLUE

Words and Music by
NEIL DIAMOND

Song sung blue ev-'ry-bo-dy knows one _____ Song sung

blue ev-'ry gar-den grows one, _____ Me and you_

are sub-ject to the blues now and then But

when you take the blues_ and make a song,_ You sing them out a-gain

Sing them out a-gain. Song sung

blue weep-ing like a wil-low _____ Song sung blue sleep-ing on my

pil-low. _____ Fun-ny thing_ but you can sing

Rhythm Tacit

— it with a cry in your voice.

And be-fore you know it start to feel-in' good, You sim - ply

got no choice.

SUMMER HOLIDAY

Words and Music by
BRUCE WELCH and BRIAN BENNETT

We're all go - ing on a sum - mer hol - i - day

No more work-ing for a week or two Fun and laugh - ter on our

sum - mer hol - i - day. No more — wor - ries for me or you,

For a week — or two. We're go - ing where the sun shines

bright - ly. We're go - ing where the sea — is blue. We've

seen it __ on the __ mov - ies, now let's see if it's true.

Ev - 'ry - bo - dy has a sum - mer hol - i - day,

Do - in' things they al - ways wan - ted to

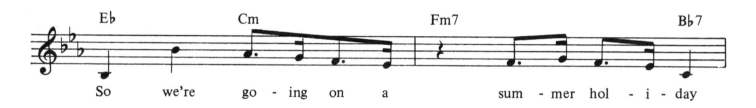

So we're go - ing on a sum - mer hol - i - day

to __ make _ our dreams come true For _ me _ and you.

THE GREEN DOOR

Words by MARVIN MOORE
Music by BOB DAVIE

Mid - night, one more night with - out sleep - in'. _____
Knocked once, tried to tell 'em I'd been there. _____

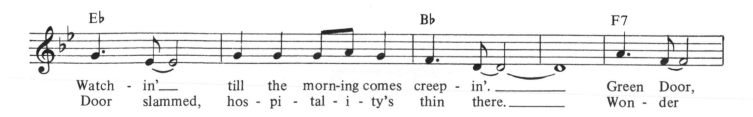

Watch - in' __ till the morn - ing comes creep - in'. _____ Green Door,
Door slammed, hos - pi - tal - i - ty's thin there. _____ Won - der

what's that se-cret you're keep - in'?_____ There's an old pi - an - o and they
just what's go-in' on in there._____ Saw an eye - ball peep - in' through a

play it hot_ be-hind the Green Door._____ Don't know what they're do - in' but they
smok - y cloud be-hind the Green Door._____ When I said, "Joe sent me," someone

laugh a lot_ be-hind the Green Door._____ Wish they'd let me in_ so I could
laughed out loud be-hind the Green Door._____ All I want to do_ is join the

find out what's be-hind the Green Door._____
hap - py crowd be-hind the Green Door._____ Ev - 'ry thing is

EVERYTHING IS BEAUTIFUL

Words and Music by
RAY STEVENS

beau - ti - ful _____ in its own way _____ Like a star - ry

sum - mer night, or a snow cov - ered win - ter's day. _____ Ev - 'ry-bod-y's

beau - ti - ful _____ in their own way _____ Un - der God's Heav - en the

world's gon - na find_____ a way. _____ Ev - 'ry-thing is _ Oh yeah.

Medley 3

RELEASE ME

Words and Music by
EDDIE MILLER, DUB WILLIAMS
ROBERT YOUNG and ROBERT HARRIS

Please re - lease me, let me go, _____ for I don't
Please re - lease me, can't you see, _____ you'd be a

love you an - y - more. To waste our
fool to cling to me. To live a

lives would be a sin, _____ re - lease me and
lie would bring us pain, _____ so re - lease me and

let me love a - gain. _____ The
let me love a - gain.

THE GREEN GREEN GRASS OF HOME

Words and Music by
CURLY PUTMAN

VERSES

old home town looks the same as I step down from the
old house is still stand - ing Tho' the paint is ___ cracked and

train, ___ and there to meet me is my Ma - ma ___ and Pa - pa
dry, ___ and theres that oak tree that I used ___ to play on ___

Down the road I looked and there runs Ma - ry, hair of gold and
Down the lane I walk with my sweet Ma - ry,

lips like cher - ies, it's good to touch the green green grass of home. Yes they'll

CHORUS

all come to meet me arms reach - ing smil-ing sweet - ly it's good to touch the

green green grass of home. The home. ____ From a Jack to a

Words and Music by
NED MILLER

FROM A JACK TO A KING

King, _____ From lon - li - ness to a wed - ding ring,

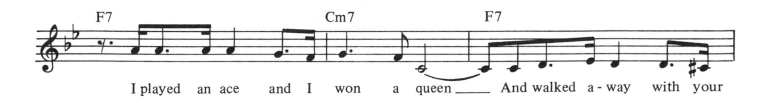

I played an ace and I won a queen ____ And walked a - way with your

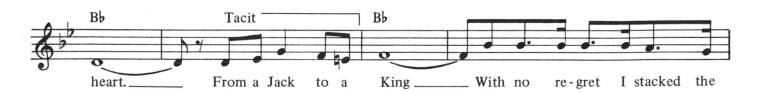

heart. _____ From a Jack to a King _____ With no re - gret I stacked the

cards last night, And la - dy luck played her hand just right ____

____ To make me king of your heart. ____ For just a lit - tle while, I

thought that I might lose the game Then just in

time, I saw the twin - kle in your eye. ____ From a Jack to a

King ____ From lon - li - ness to a wed - ding ring,

I played an ace and I won a queen, You made me queen of your

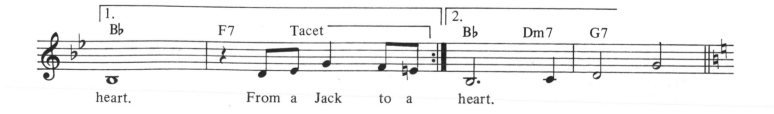

heart. From a Jack to a heart.

KING OF THE ROAD

Words and Music by
ROGER MILLER

1.3. Trail - er ___ for sale ___ or rent ___   Rooms ___ to let
2. Third box ___ car mid - night train ___   Des - ti - na - tion

fif - ty   cents ___   No phone, no pool, ___ no pets, ___
Ban - gor,   Maine ___   Old worn ___ out suit ___ and shoes ___

I ain't got no ci - gar - ettes, ___ Ah but two hours ___ of
I don't pay no Un - ion dues, ___ I smoke old sto - gies

push - in' broom ___ buys a   eight ___ by twelve
I have found ___   short, ___ but not too

four bit room, ___ } I'm a man of means ___ by ___ no means ___
big a - round, ___ }

King of the road. ___   King of the road. ___

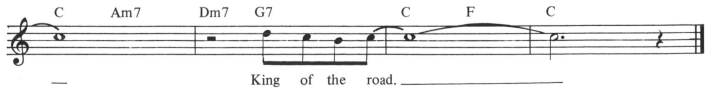

—   King of the road. ___

Medley 4

MOON RIVER

Words by JOHNNY MERCER
Music by HENRY MANCINI

SEE THE DAY

Words and Music by
D. C. LEE

Ev - er See The Day? Heart-ache leads a - stray.

Good love will al - ways come from me. Will you ev - er learn to

love with - out a lit - tle doubt?_____ Good love will al - ways

come from me._____ Will you_____

CHARMAINE

Words by LOU POLLACK
Music by ERNO RAPEE

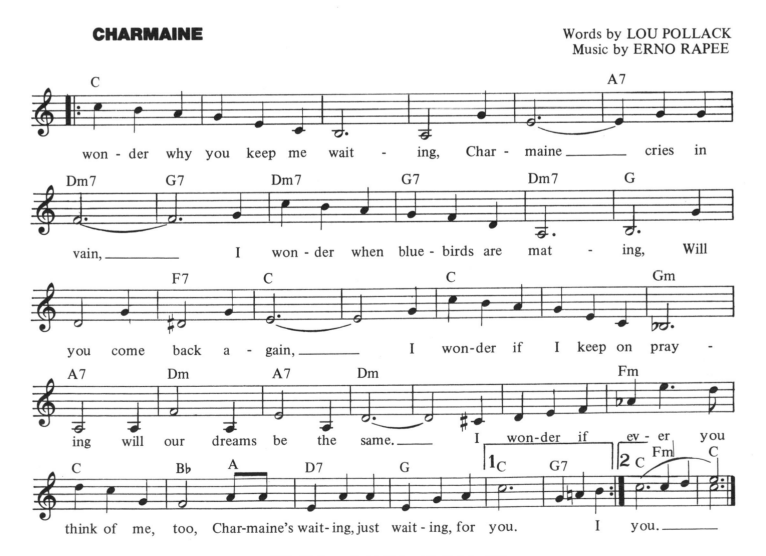

won - der why you keep me wait - ing, Char - maine _____ cries in

vain, _____ I won - der when blue - birds are mat - ing, Will

you come back a - gain, _____ I won-der if I keep on pray -

ing will our dreams be the same. _____ I won-der if ev - er you

think of me, too, Char-maine's wait-ing, just wait - ing, for you. I you. _____

Medley 5

YOU'RE A PINK TOOTHBRUSH

Words and Music by
DICK JAMES, BOB HALFIN
RALPH RUVIN and HAROLD IRVING

You're a

pink tooth - brush I'm a blue tooth - brush, Have we met some - where be -

fore? You're a pink tooth - brush, And I think tooth - brush that we

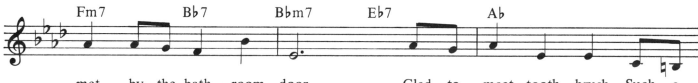

met by the bath - room door, Glad to meet tooth - brush, Such a

sweet tooth - brush, How you thrill me thru', and thru' Don't be

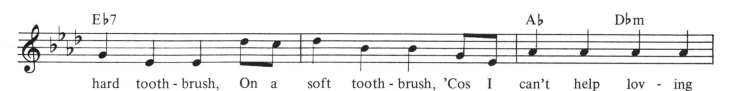

hard tooth - brush, On a soft tooth - brush, 'Cos I can't help lov - ing

you. Ev - 'ry time I hear you whist - le.

(Whistle ....) You make my ny - lon brist - le.

(Whistle . . . . Wolf wistle) You're a pink tooth-brush, I'm a

blue tooth-brush, Won't you mar-ry me in haste, I'll be true tooth-brush, Just to

you tooth-brush, When we both use the same tooth-paste. You need

YOU NEED HANDS

Words and Music by
ROY IRWIN

hands to hold some-one you care for_____ You need hands to

show that you're sin-cere_____ When you feel no-bo-dy wants to

know you_____ You need hands to brush a-way the tears_____ When you

hold a brand new ba-by,_____ You need ten-der hands to

guide them on their way_____ You need hands to thank the Lord for

liv-ing_____ And for giv-ing us this day. I'll take the

THE DUMMY SONG

Words by LEW BROWN & BILLY ROSE
Music by RAY HENDERSON

Medley 6

LILY THE PINK

Adapted and Arranged by
GORMAN, McGEAR and McGOUGH

We'll

drink a drink a drink to Li - ly the pink the pink the pink the sav - iour

of _____ the hu - man race _____ For she in -

vent - ed _____ me - di - ci - nal com - pound _____ Most ef - fi -

ca - cious _____ in ev - 'ry case _____ Mis - ter

Fl - ears _____ had stick - ing out ears _____ And it
To - ny _____ was known to be bon - ey _____ He would

made him aw - ful shy _____ And so they
nev - er eat his meals _____

gave him me - di - ci - nal com - pound
Now he's learn - ing _____
Now they move him

1 how to fly _____ Bro - ther wheels
2 round on wheels _____ We'll

drink a drink a drink to Li - ly the pink the pink the pink the sav - iour of _____

_____ the hu - man race _____ For she in - vent - ed _____ me - di - ci - nal

com - pound _____ Most ef - fi - ca - cious _____ in ev - 'ry case. _____

TIE ME KANGAROO DOWN SPORT

Words and Music by
ROLF HARRIS

Watch me wal - la - by's feed, mate, Watch me wal - la - by's

feed. They're a dan - ger - ous breed, mate, So watch me wal - la - by's

feed. Al - to - geth - er now. Tie me kan - ga - roo down, sport,

Tie me kan - ga - roo down, Tie me kan - ga - roo down, sport,

Tie me kan - ga - roo down, Al - to - geth - er now. down. Oh this

Y VIVA ESPANA (EVIVA ESPANA)

Original Words by LEO ROZENSTRAETEN
English Words by EDDIE SEAGO
Music by LEO CAERTS

Medley 7

IN THE NAVY

Words and Music by
J. MORALI, H. BELOLO and V. WILLIS

In the na - vy___ yes, you can

sail the sev - en seas _ in the na - vy___ yes, you can

put your mind at ease _ (in the na - vy) ___ come on now,

peo - ple make a stand (in the na - vy) can't you see we need a hand. (in the

na - vy) ___ come on, pro - tect the moth-er - land _ (in the

na - vy) ___ come on and join your fel - low man _ (in the

na - vy) ___ come on peo - ple and make a stand _ (in the

na - vy,) in the na - vy, in the na - vy. In the na - vy.

D.I.S.C.O.

Words and Music by
DANIEL VANGARDE and JEAN KLUGER

D. I. S. C. O. D. I. S. C. O. D. I.. S. C. O.

D. I. S. C. O. She is D. She is

I. She is S. She is C. She is O. ___ She is

To Coda (Instr.)

She is

She is

D. I. S. C. O. D. I. S. C. O. D. I. S. C. O.

D. I. S. C. O.

Y.M.C.A.

Words and Music by
J. MORALI, H, BELOLO and V. WILLIS

Young man, there's no need to feel down. I said young man pick your-
Young man, I was once in your shoes. I said I was down and

self off the ground. I said Young man 'cause you're in a new town there's no
out with the blues. I felt no man cared if I were a-live, I felt

Medley 8

TIE A YELLOW RIBBON

Words and Music by
IRVINE LEVINE and LARRY BROWN

I'm com-ing home __ I've done my time, __ Now I've got to know what is __ and is - n't mine __ If you re - ceived my let - ter tel - lin' you __ I'd soon be free Then you'll know just what __ to do __ If you still want me. If you still love me __ Well tie a yel - low rib - bon round the ole oak tree it's been three long years do ya still want me? If

I don't see a rib-bon 'round the ole oak tree.__ I'll
stay on the bus, For-get a-bout us, put the blame on me, If
I don't see a yel-low rib-bon 'round the ole __ oak

1 tree. _____

2 tree. _____

YELLOW BIRD

Words by MARILYN KEITH and ALAN BERGMAN
Music by NORMAN LUBOFF

Yel - low Bird, up high in ba-na-na tree. Yel - low

Bird, you sit all a - lone like me. Did your la - dy frien'
Bet - ter fly__ a - way

leave de nest__ a - gain? Dat is ve - ry sad, make me feel__ so bad.
in de sky__ a - way. Pick - er com - in' soon, pick from night__ to noon.

You can fly__ a - way, in the sky__ a - way. You more luck - y dan me!
Black an' yel - low you, like ba - na - na too. Dey might pick you some day!

Yel - low Bird   Yel - low Bird

Yel - low   Bird. _____ There's a

THE YELLOW ROSE OF TEXAS

TRADITIONAL

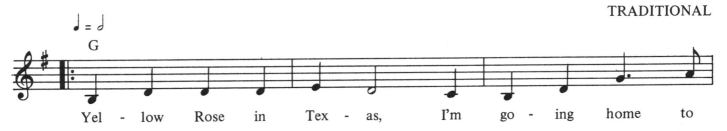

Yel - low Rose in Tex - as, I'm go - ing home to

see, She wants no ot - her fel - low, No - bod - y else but

me. Oh she cried so when I left her that it

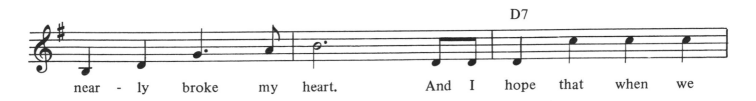

near - ly broke my heart. And I hope that when we

meet a - gain, we nev - er more will part. There's a part.

SHE WORE A YELLOW RIBBON

TRADITIONAL

Medley 9

OH WHAT A BEAUTIFUL MORNING

Words by OSCAR HAMMERSTEIN II
Music by RICHARD RODGERS

CHORUS

Oh what a beau - ti - ful morn - ing. Oh what a
beau - ti - ful day. _____ Oh what a beau - ti - ful
feel - in' Ev - 'ry - things go - in' my way. _____
_____ Ev - 'ry - things go - in' my way.

MY FAVOURITE THINGS

Words by OSCAR HAMMERSTEIN II
Music by RICHARD RODGERS

Rain - drops on ros - es and whisk - ers on kit - tens,
Cream col - ored pon - ies and crisp ap - ple strud - els,

Bright cop - per ket - tles and warm wool - en mit - tens,
Door - bells and sleigh - bells and schnitz - el with noo - dles,

Brown pa - per pack - ag - es tied up with string,
Wild geese that fly with the moon on their wings,

These are a few of my fa - vour - ite things.
These are a few of my fa - vour - ite things.

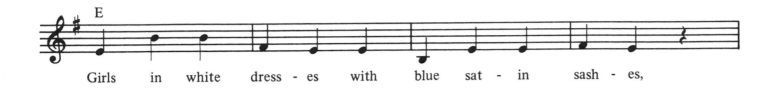

Girls in white dress - es with blue sat - in sash - es,

Snow - flakes that stay on my nose and eye - lash - es,

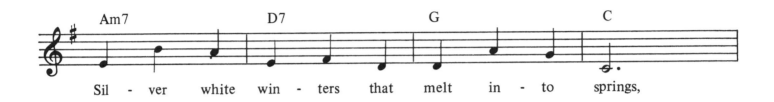

Sil - ver white win - ters that melt in - to springs,

These are a few of my fa - vor - ite things. It's a

IT'S A GRAND NIGHT FOR SINGING

Words by OSCAR HAMMERSTEIN II
Music by RICHARD RODGERS

grand night for sing - ing! The

moon is fly - ing high _____ And

some - where a bird who is bound he'll be heard, Is

throw - ing his heart at the sky. It's a

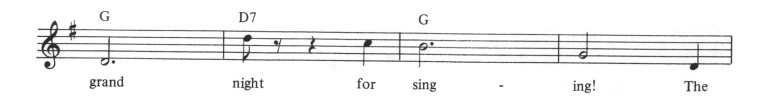

grand night for sing - ing! The

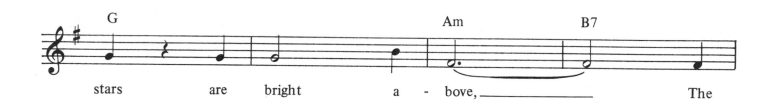

stars are bright a - bove, _____ The

earth is a glow and to add to the

show, I think I am fall - ing in

love. _____ Fall - ing,

Fall - ing in love. _____

EDELWEISS

Words by OSCAR HAMMERSTEIN II
Music by RICHARD RODGERS

Medley 10

LOVE OF THE COMMON PEOPLE

Words and Music by
JOHN HURLEY and RONNIE WILKINS

Liv - ing on free feed tick - ets, Wat - er in the milk from a

hole in the roof where the rain came thru'. What can you

do? _____ Tears from the lit - tle sis - ter;

Cry - ing 'cause she does - n't have a dress with - out a patch for the

par - ty to go. But you know___ she'll get by,_

_ 'cause she's liv - ing in the love of the com - mon peo - ple,

Smile's from the heart of a fam - i - ly man.___

Dad - dy's gon - na buy you a dream to cling ____ to,

Ma - ma's gon - na love you just as much as she can, _____

And she can. _____ 'Cause you're

can. _____ Ev - er - y

YEH YEH

Words and Music by
GRANT, PATRICK and HENDRICKS

eve - nin'   when all my day's work is thru'   I call my
loves me,   she gets me feel - in' so fine.   The way she

ba - by   and ask her "what should we do?"   I men - tion
loves me,   she makes me know that she's mine.   And when she

mo - vies,   but she don't seem to dig that.   And then she
kiss - es   I feel the fire ____ get hot.   She nev - er

asks me   why don't I come to her flat   and have some
miss - es   she gives it all that she's got.   And when she

KNOCK THREE TIMES

Words and Music by
IRWIN LEVINE and L. RUSSELL BROWN

Knock Three Times on the ceil-ing if you want_ me;_____

Twice on the pipe if the an-swer is no._____

Oh, my sweet-ness, Knock Knock Knock means you'll meet me in the

hall - way;_____ Twice on the pipe

means you ain't gon - na show._____

Medley 11

WHAT A WONDERFUL WORLD

Words and Music by
GEORGE DAVID WEISS and BOB THIELE

friends shak - in' hands, ___ say - in', "How do you do!"

They're real - ly say - in' "I love you," I hear ba - bies cry, I

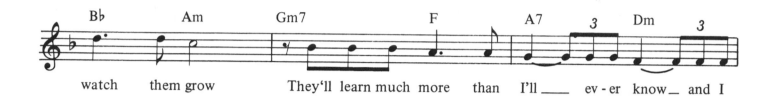

watch them grow They'll learn much more than I'll ___ ev - er know ___ and I

think ___ to my-self what a won - der - ful world. ___ Yes, I

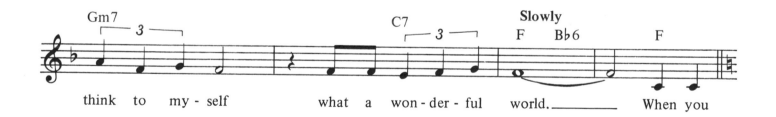

think to my - self what a won - der - ful world. ___ When you

YOU'LL NEVER WALK ALONE

Words by OSCAR HAMMERSTEIN II
Music by RICHARD RODGERS

walk through a storm, hold your head up high And

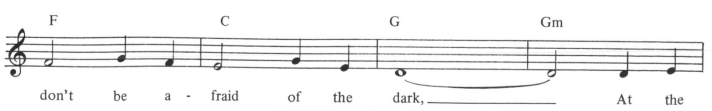

don't be a - fraid of the dark, ___ At the

end of the storm is a gold - en sky And the

sweet sil - ver song of a lark. _____ Walk

on through the wind, Walk on through the rain, Tho' your

dreams be tossed and blown _____ Walk

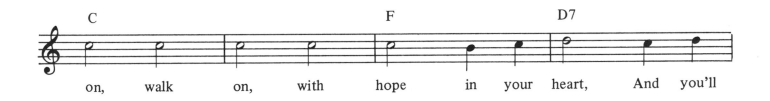

on, walk on, with hope in your heart, And you'll

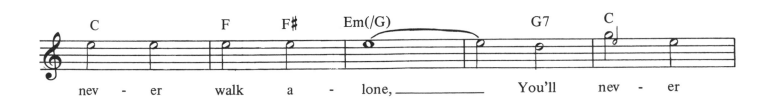

nev - er walk a - lone, _____ You'll nev - er

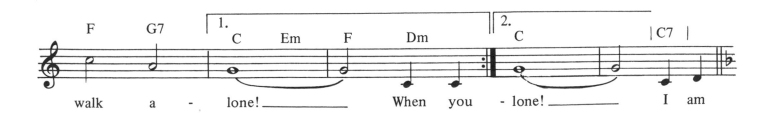

walk a - lone! _____ When you - lone! _____ I am

SAILING

Words and Music by
GAVIN SUTHERLAND

Sail - ing,_____ I am sail - ing,_____ home a - gain _____ 'cross the
Fly - ing,_____ I am fly - ing,_____ like a bird _____ 'cross the
Hear me,_____ Can you hear me _____ thru' the dark - night _____ far a -

sea._____ I am sail - ing _____ storm - y wa - ters,_____ To be
sky._____ I am fly - ing _____ pass - ing high clouds,_____ To be
way._____ I am dy - ing _____ For ev - er try - ing _____ To be

near_ you_____ to be free._____ I am
with_ you_____ to be free._____ Can you
with_ you_____ who can _____ say.

hear me_____ Can you hear me,_____ 'Thro the dark_____ night_____
sail - ing_____ We are sail - ing,_____ Home a - gain _____

— far a - way. _____ I am dy - ing _____ for - ev - er
— 'cross the sea _____ We are sail - ing _____ storm - y

try - ing _____ To be with_ you _____ who can say _____
wa - ters,_____ To be near_ you _____ to be free _____

— We are to be free. _____
— To be near_ you _____ to be

near you_____ to be free. _____

Medley 12

SAVE YOUR KISSES FOR ME

Words and Music by
TONY HILLIER, MARTIN LEE
and LEE SHERIDEN

Save your kiss-es for me, __ save all your kiss-es for me __ Bye-bye, ba-by bye-bye __ Don't cry hon-ey, don't cry __ Gon-na walk out the door __ but I'll soon be back for more Kiss-es for me __ save all your kiss-es for me __ so long hon-ey, so long. __ Hang on ba-by, hang on __ don't you dare me to stay __ 'cos you know you've got to save your kiss-es for me, __ save all your kiss-es for me __ Bye-bye, ba-by bye-bye

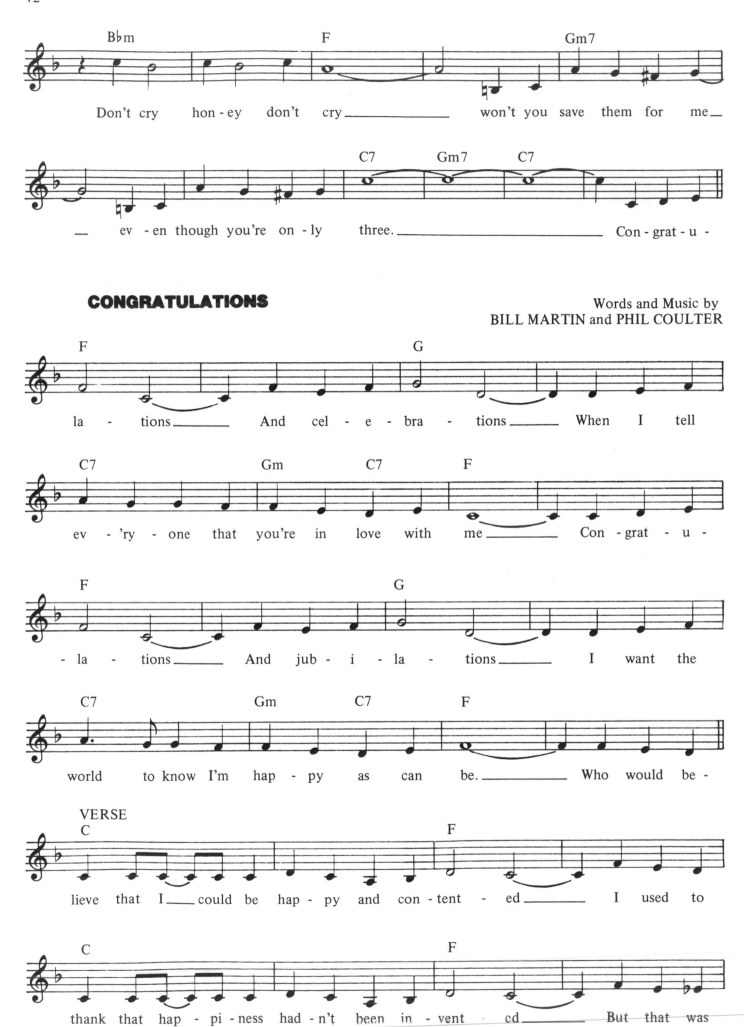

Don't cry hon-ey don't cry _____ won't you save them for me ____ ev-en though you're on-ly three. _____ Con-grat-u-

CONGRATULATIONS

Words and Music by
BILL MARTIN and PHIL COULTER

la - tions _____ And cel-e-bra-tions _____ When I tell ev-'ry-one that you're in love with me _____ Con-grat-u- la-tions _____ And jub-i-la-tions _____ I want the world to know I'm hap-py as can be. _____ Who would be-

VERSE

lieve that I ____ could be hap-py and con-tent-ed _____ I used to thank that hap-pi-ness had-n't been in-vent-ed _____ But that was

D ... **Gm7**

in the bad old days be-fore I met you ___ When I let you ___

C7

___ walk in-to my heart. ___ Con-grat-u

CHORUS
F ... **G**

la - tions ___ And cel-e-bra-tions ___ When I tell

C **Gm** **C7** **F**

ev-'ry-one that you're in love with me ___ Con-grat-u

F **G**

la - tions ___ And jub-i-la-tions ___ I want the

C **Gm** **C7** **F** **Bb7**

world to know I'm hap-py as can be ___

PUPPET ON A STRING

Words and Music by
BILL MARTIN and PHIL COULTER

Eb ... **Bb7**

I ___ won-der if one day that you'll

Eb **Bb7**

say that you care, If you'd say you love me mad-ly, I'd glad-ly be

there, Like a pup-pet on a string _____

Love is just like a mer-ry-go-round_ With all the
One day I'm feel-ing down on the ground_ Then I'm

fun of the fair. _____ } Are you lead-ing me on?_____
up in the air. _____

___ To - mor - row will you be gone?_____

CHORUS

I _____ won - der if one day that you'll

say that you care, If you'd say you love me mad - ly, I'd

glad - ly be there, Like a pup-pet on a string._____

_____ Like a pup - pet on a string.

Medley 13

POSTMAN PAT

Words and Music by
BRYAN DALY

Animato

C | G | F | G

CHORUS

C | Am

Post - man Pat, Post - man, Pat, Post - man Pat and his black and white cat.___

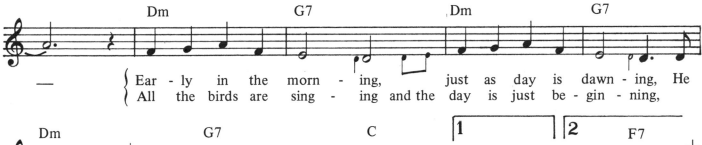

Dm | G7 | Dm | G7

Ear - ly in the morn - ing, just as day is dawn - ing, He
All the birds are sing - ing and the day is just be - gin - ning,

Dm | G7 | C | 1 | 2 | F7

picks up all the post - bags in his van.___
Pat feels he's a real - ly hap - py man.___

© 1982 & 1986 : Post Music Ltd., 14 Parkway, Welwyn Garden City, Herts AL8 6HB.

PUFF THE MAGIC DRAGON

Words and Music by
PETER YARROW and LEONARD LIPTON

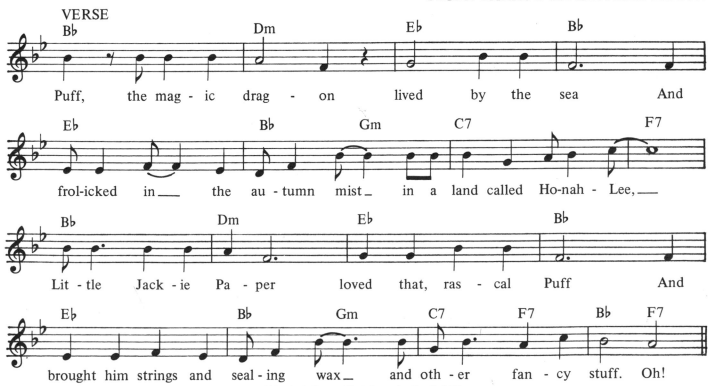

VERSE

Bb | Dm | Eb | Bb

Puff, the mag - ic drag - on lived by the sea And

Eb | Bb | Gm | C7 | F7

frol - icked in___ the au - tumn mist___ in a land called Ho-nah - Lee,___

Bb | Dm | Eb | Bb

Lit - tle Jack - ie Pa - per loved that, ras - cal Puff And

Eb | Bb | Gm | C7 | F7 | Bb | F7

brought him strings and seal - ing wax___ and oth - er fan - cy stuff. Oh!

© 1962 and 1985 Pepamar Music Corporation, New York, NY
Warner Bros Music Ltd, 17 Berners Street, London W1P 3DD, for the British Commonwealth of Nations
(excluding Canada and Australasia) and Republic of Ireland

REFRAIN

Bb / Dm / Eb

Puff, the mag - ic drag - on lived by the

Bb / Eb / Bb Gm

sea And frol - icked in __ the au - tumn mist __ in a

C7 / F7 / Bb

land called Ho - nah - Lee, __ Puff, the mag - ic

Dm / Eb / Bb / Eb

drag - on lived by the sea And frol - icked in __ the

Bb Gm / C7 F7 / Bb

au - tumn mist __ in a land called Ho - nah - Lee.

GROCER JACK

Words and Music by
C. PHILWIT and KEITH HOPKINS

Eb / Bb / Ab / Eb

Gro - cer Jack, gro - cer Jack, get off your back, get in - to town, don't

Gm Cm

let them down, ___ Oh no, ___ no. ___

Eb / Bb / Ab / Eb

Gro - cer Jack, gro - cer Jack, get off your back, get in - to town, don't

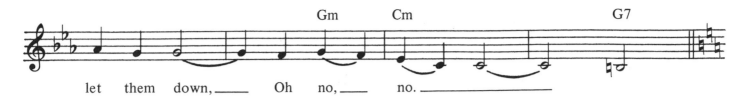

DO-RE-MI

Words by OSCAR HAMMERSTEIN II
Music by RICHARD RODGERS

Medley 14

WHAT HAVE THEY DONE TO OUR SONG MA

Words and Music by
MELANIE SAFKA

1.2. Look what they've done ___ to my song ___ Ma,
3. La la la la ___ la la la ___ la

Look what they've done to my song Well it's the
La la la la la la la la la la Well they

on - ly thing ___ that I could do half right, And it's turn - in' out all
tied it up ___ in a plas - tic bag, And turned it up - side
la la la ___ la la la la la la la la la la la la la

wrong Ma
down Ma } Look what they've done ___ to my song
la la Look what they've done ___ to my song

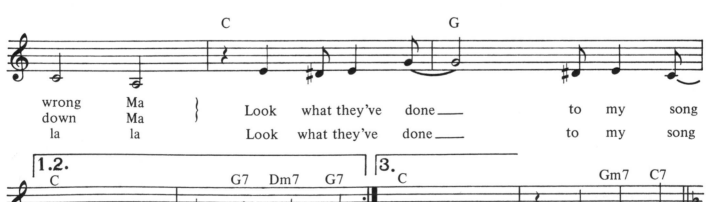

DAYS OF WINE AND ROSES

Words by JOHNNY MERCER
Music by HENRY MANCINI

TRAIL OF THE LONESOME PINE

Words by BALLAD MACDONALD
Music by HARRY CARROLL

Blue Ridge Mount-ains of Vir - gin - ia, On the trail of the lone - some

pine. In the pale moon-shine our hearts en - twine, Where she carved her name and

I carved mine. Oh, June! like the mount-ains I'm blue, Like the pine I am

lone - some for you,_ In the Blue Ridge Mount - ains of Vir - gin - ia On the

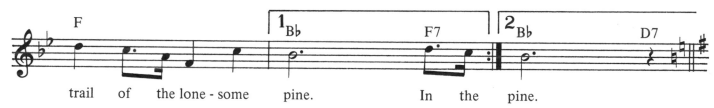

trail of the lone - some pine. In the pine.

SPANISH EYES

Words by CHARLES SINGLETON
and EDDIE SNYDER
Music by BERT KAEMPFERT

Moderato

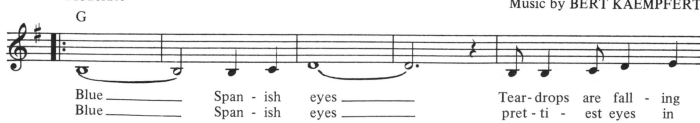

Blue _____ Span - ish eyes _____ Tear-drops are fall - ing
Blue _____ Span - ish eyes _____ pret - ti - est eyes in

from your Span - ish eyes_____ Please, _____ please don't
all of Mex - i - co _____ True _____ Span - ish

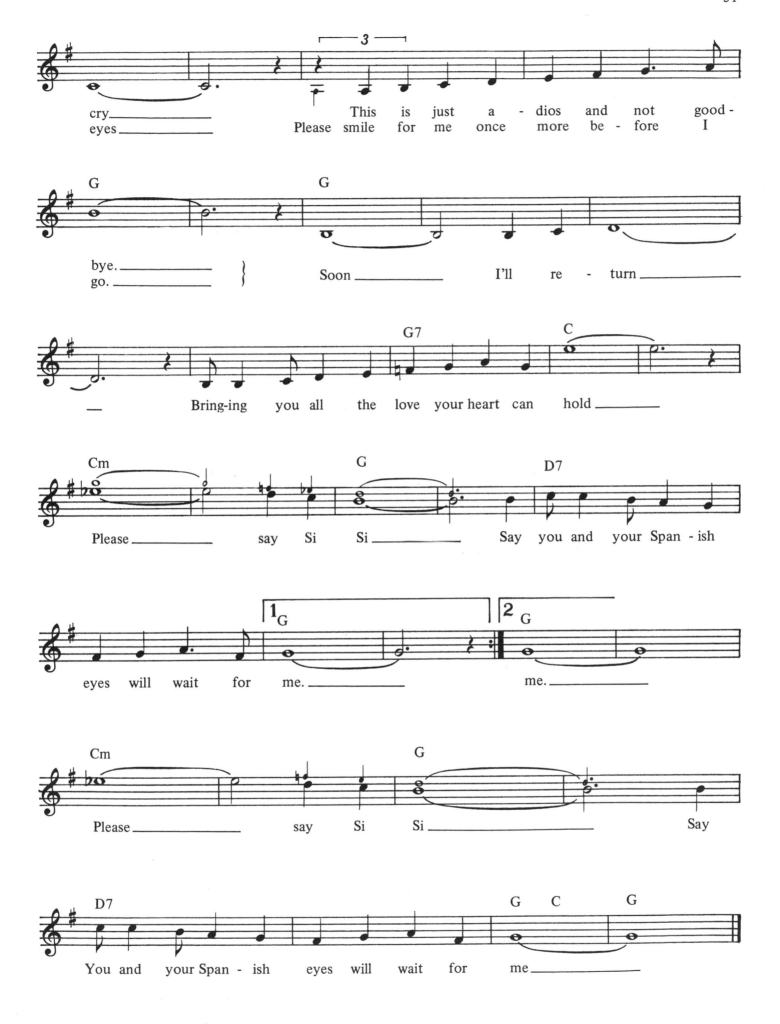

Medley 15

THE OLD FASHIONED WAY (Les Plaisirs Demodes)

Original Lyrics CHARLES AZNOVOUR
English Words by AL KASHA and JOEL HIRSCHHORN
Music by GEORGE GARVARENTEZ

Dance ___ in the old fash-ioned way. ___ Won't you stay in my arms? ___

___ { Just melt a-gainst my skin And let me feel your
{ And we'll dis-cov-er highs We nev-er knew be-

heart, Don't let the mu-sic win By danc-ing far a-part. ___
fore, If we just close our eyes And dance a-round the floor, ___

— Come close ___ where you be-long. ___ Let's
— That gay ___ old fash-ioned

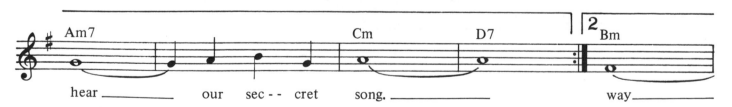

hear ___ our sec---cret song. ___ way ___

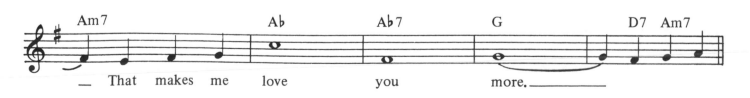

— That makes me love you more. ___

BYE BYE BLUES

Words and Music by
DAVE BENNETT & FRED HAMM

YOURS

Original Lyrics by AUGUSTIN RODRIGUEZ
Words by JACK SHEER
Music by GONZALO ROIG

3 O'CLOCK IN THE MORNING

Words by DOROTHY TERRISS
Music by JULIAN SLADE

Medley 16

SIMON SAYS

Words and Music by
ELLIOT CHIPRUT

Verse 2

Simple Simon says put your hands on your hips,
Let your backbone slip, Simon says.
Simple Simon says put your hands on your hips,
Let your backbone slip, Simon says.

Chorus

Put your hands on hips (Simple Simon says),
Bring them down by your side (Simple Simon says),
Shake them to your left (Simple Simon says),
Now shake them to your right.

Verse 3

Now that you have learned to play this game with me,
You can see it's not so hard to do.
Let's try it once again this time more carefully,
And I hope the winner will be you.

Chorus

Clap your hands in the air (Simple Simon says),
Do it double time (Simple Simon says),
Then slow it down like before (Simple Simon says),
Ah - you're looking fine.

BIRDIE SONG

Words and Music by
WERNER THOMAS and TERRY RENDELL

Da da da da da da da da etc.

Da da da da da da

Printed in Great Britain by Hobbs the Printers Ltd, Totton, Hampshire 9/98